y as in jelly

A Making words

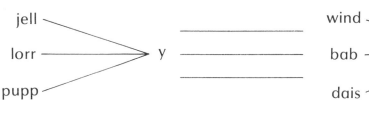

jell ——
lorr —— > y _____
pupp —— _____

happ ——
funn —— > y _____
bus —— _____

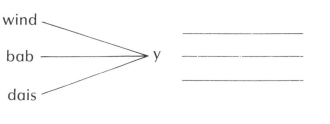

wind ——
bab —— > y _____
dais —— _____

sunn ——
hill —— > y _____
hurr —— _____

B Choose from the twelve words you have made. Write the correct word under each picture.

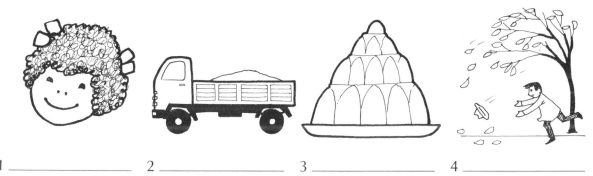

1 _____ 2 _____ 3 _____ 4 _____

C Complete the sentences, using words you have made.

1 A _____ is a young dog.

2 The clowns at the circus were very _____.

3 We'll have to _____ or we'll be late for school.

4 The _____ is asleep in the cot.

D Word meanings

Across

1 large vehicle

2 breezy

3 when the sun shines it is _____

4 having a lot to do

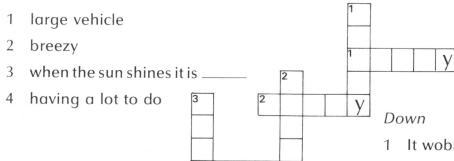

Down

1 It wobbles when we eat it!

2 mountainous

3 small white flower, found in grass

1

ey as in key

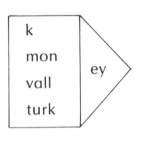

A Making words

k
mon
vall
turk
> ey

_____
_____
_____
_____

journ
donk
gr
pr
> ey

_____
_____
_____
_____

parsl
jock
hon
monk
ob
> ey

_____
_____
_____
_____
_____

abb
hock
jers
barl
chimn
> ey

_____
_____
_____
_____
_____

B Choose from the eighteen words you have made. Write the correct word under each picture.

1 _____   2 _____   3 _____   4 _____

C Complete the sentences, using words you have made.

1 We use _____ to buy things.

2 The colour of a rainy sky is _____.

3 A _____ is a person paid to ride a horse in a race.

4 It is a long _____ from London to Moscow.

5 We walked down the hill into the _____.

D Word meanings

1 sweet, sticky, yellow liquid made by bees

2 to do what you are told

3 knitted, long sleeved pullover

4 animal hunted and eaten by other animals

			e	y
			e	y
			e	y
			e	y

2

$\boxed{\text{ei}}$ as in veil

A Making words

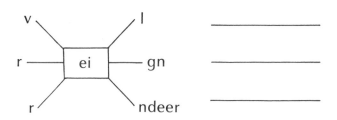

v   l
r — ei — gn
r   ndeer
_____
_____
_____

n   gh
r   ns
v   ei   ns
s   ze
_____
_____
_____
_____

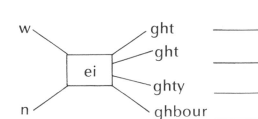

w   ght
   ght
ei
   ghty
n   ghbour
_____
_____
_____
_____

sl   gh
rec   ve
  ei
c   ling
dec   ve
_____
_____
_____
_____

B Choose from the fifteen words you have made. Write the correct word under each picture.

1 _____   2 _____   3 _____   4 _____

C Complete the sentences, using words you have made.

1 The vessels in your body which carry blood to the heart are called _____.

2 How many presents did you _____ on your birthday?

3 The rider stopped the horse by pulling the _____.

4 An octopus has _____ arms.

5 Our next door _____ is an elderly lady.

D Word meanings

1 call or cry of a horse

2 to make someone believe something untrue

3 length of time a king or queen rules

4 inside roof of a room

				e	i		
			e	i			
				e	i		
	e	i					

3

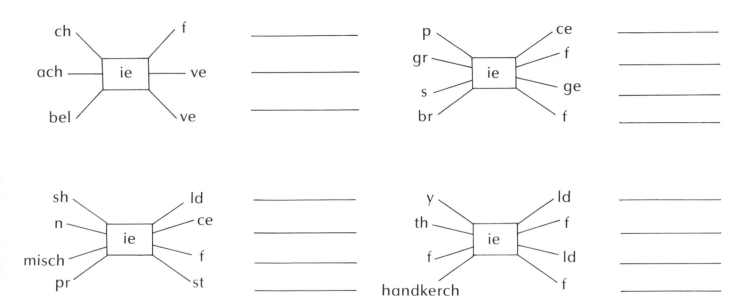

ie as in chief

A Making words

ch
ach —— ie —— ve
bel
f
ve

_____
_____
_____
_____

p
gr
s
br
ie
ce
f
ge
f

_____
_____
_____
_____

sh
n
misch
pr
ie
ld
ce
f
st

_____
_____
_____
_____

y
th
f
ie
ld
f
ld
handkerch
f

_____
_____
_____
_____

B Choose from the fifteen words you have made. Write the correct word under each picture.

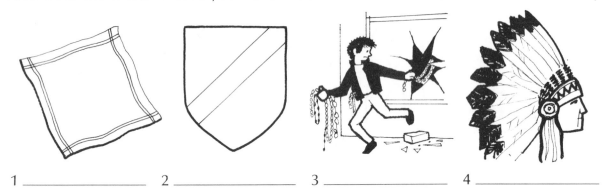

1 _____   2 _____   3 _____   4 _____

C Complete the sentences, using words you have made.

1 A farmer grows crops in a _____.

2 Bob ate a large _____ of birthday cake.

3 Joan wrote a _____ thank you note to her aunt for the present.

4 The brave soldiers would not _____ to the enemy.

5 Sam was called a _____ by his mother because he was getting in her way.

D Word meanings

1 to think something is true

2 daughter of your brother or sister

3 minister or clergyman

4 sorrow; sadness

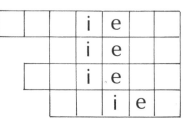

4

ck as in duck

A Making words

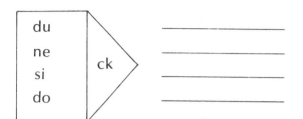

du
ne
si
do
ck ——————
——————
——————
——————

ki
lu
ro
li
ck ——————
——————
——————
——————

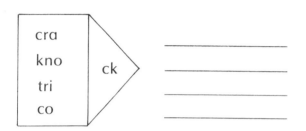

cra
kno
tri
co
ck ——————
——————
——————
——————

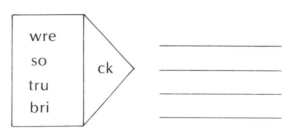

wre
so
tru
bri
ck ——————
——————
——————
——————

B Choose from the sixteen words you have made. Write the correct word under each picture:

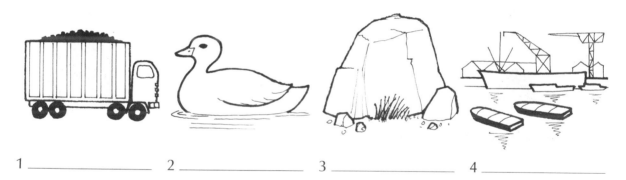

1 _____ 2 _____ 3 _____ 4 _____

C Complete the sentences, using words you have made.

1 Pam wore a scarf round her _____ to keep her warm.

2 The postman gave a loud _____ on the door.

3 The _____ of the ship lay on the rocky beach.

4 The dog began to _____ its lips when it saw the bone.

5 The magician's first _____ was to pull a rabbit out of a hat.

D Word meanings

1 male bird

2 block of baked clay used in building

3 something happening by chance, either good or bad

4 ill; unwell

			c	k
			c	k
			c	k
			c	k

[el] as in camel

A Making words

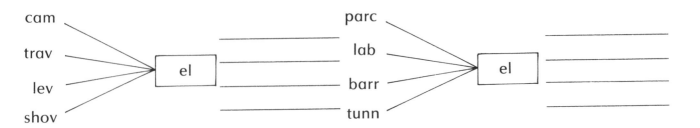

cam
trav → [el] _____
lev _____
shov _____

parc
lab → [el] _____
barr _____
tunn _____

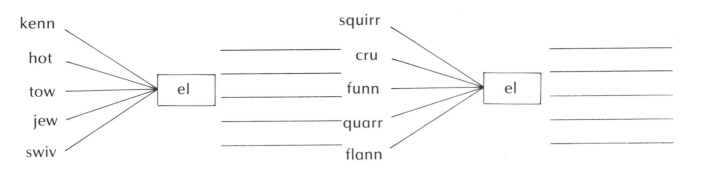

kenn
hot
tow → [el] _____
jew _____
swiv _____

squirr
cru
funn → [el] _____
quarr _____
flann _____

B Choose from the eighteen words you have made. Write the correct word under each picture.

1 _____   2 _____   3 _____   4 _____

C Complete the sentences, using words you have made.

1 Mark has to _____ two miles to school each day.

2 A _____ is a rare stone, such as a diamond.

3 A _____ can go without drinking water for many days in the desert.

4 The boys began to _____ about who had won the game.

5 The postman brought a large _____ to our house.

D Word meanings

1 piece of thick cloth used to dry things

2 round, wooden container

3 chimney on a ship

4 building where people pay for a bedroom and food

			e	l
			e	l
			e	l
			e	l

6

le as in table

A   Making words

tab
whist
trif   > le   _____
litt   _____
                    _____
                    _____

app
bott   > le   _____
peop   _____
midd   _____
                   _____

terrib
hand   > le   _____
ank   _____
tremb   _____
cast   _____

pudd
cand   > le   _____
bicyc   _____
grumb   _____
eag   _____

B   Choose from the eighteen words you have made. Write the correct word under each picture.

  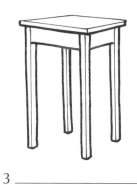 

1 _____   2 _____   3 _____   4 _____

C   Complete the sentences, using words you have made.

1   The referee blew his _____ to stop the game.

2   After the heavy rain there was a large _____ outside the door.

3   A large number of _____ live in a city.

4   There is usually a white line in the _____ of main roads.

5   The wind made the leaves on the tree _____ .

D   Word meanings

1   part of your leg, between the foot and the calf

2   to find fault; complain

3   fruit which is good for your teeth!

4   opposite of big

			l	e
			l	e
			l	e
			l	e

[et] as in bucket

A Making words

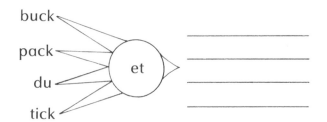

buck
pack
du
tick

_____
_____
_____
_____

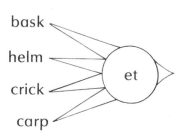

bask
helm
crick
carp

_____
_____
_____
_____

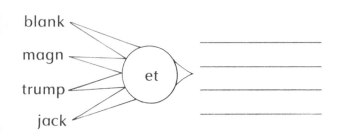

blank
magn
trump
jack

_____
_____
_____
_____

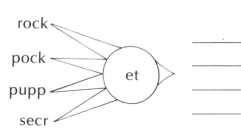

rock
pock
pupp
secr

_____
_____
_____
_____

B Choose from the sixteen words you have made. Write the correct word under each picture.

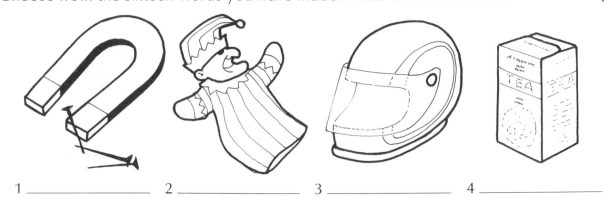

1 _____ 2 _____ 3 _____ 4 _____

C Complete the sentences, using words you have made.

1 Our muddy shoes made the _____ dirty.

2 The _____ is a musical instrument sounded by blowing.

3 Carol has a _____ hiding place where she keeps her sweets.

4 You have to buy a _____ before you go on the train.

5 A _____ is useful for carrying shopping.

D Word meanings

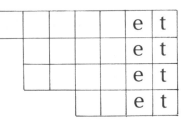

1 game played with bats, wickets and a ball

2 small bag sewed into clothes for holding things

3 short coat

4 piece of music played or sung by two people

A Making words

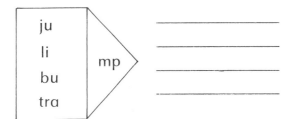

ju
li
bu
tra
mp
_____
_____
_____
_____

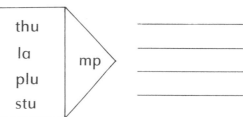

thu
la
plu
stu
mp
_____
_____
_____
_____

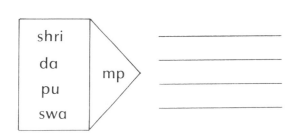

shri
da
pu
swa
mp
_____
_____
_____
_____

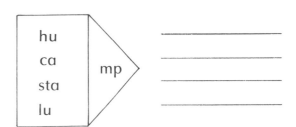

hu
ca
sta
lu
mp
_____
_____
_____
_____

B Choose from the sixteen words you have made. Write the correct word under each picture.

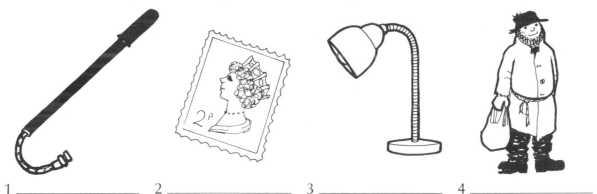

1 _____ 2 _____ 3 _____ 4 _____

C Complete the sentences, using words you have made.

1 Joan started to _____ because her heel was sore.

2 The shower of rain made the grass _____, so we couldn't sit on it.

3 Sheila won the high _____ in the school sports.

4 The Scouts made their _____ in a field near a farm.

5 Barry ran into the wall and got a _____ on his head.

D Word meanings

1 to hit something, making a heavy sound

2 small shellfish

3 rather fat; chubby

4 wet, marshy land

			m	p
			m	p
			m	p
			m	p

qu as in queue

A Making words

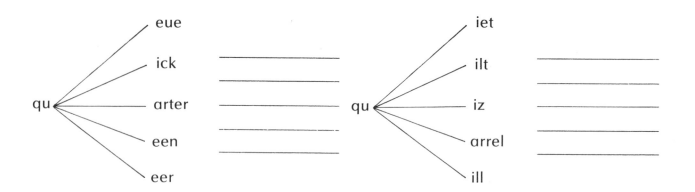

qu — eue
qu — ick
qu — arter
qu — een
qu — eer

_____
_____
_____
_____
_____

qu — iet
qu — ilt
qu — iz
qu — arrel
qu — ill

_____
_____
_____
_____
_____

B Choose from the ten words you have made. Write the correct word under each picture.

1 _____ 2 _____ 3 _____ 4 _____

C Complete the sentences, using words you have made.

1 We had to wait for ages in the _____ for the bus.

2 Be _____! Everyone is asleep.

3 The _____ lives in a palace.

4 Jane and Sue had a terrible _____, but they're friends again now.

5 Peter has a warm new _____ on his bed.

D Word meanings

1 test of general knowledge

2 rather strange; odd

3 fast

4 pen made from a feather

5 fraction

6 argument

q	u				
q	u				
q	u				
q	u				
q	u				
q	u				

⬛ squ as in **squeak**

A Word meanings

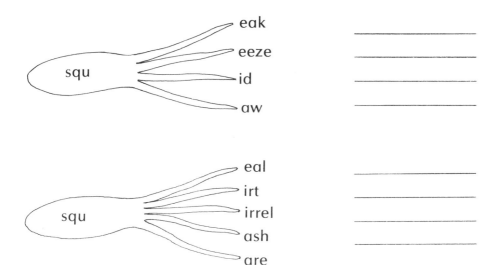

squ — eak _____
— eeze _____
— id _____
— aw _____

squ — eal _____
— irt _____
— irrel _____
— ash _____
— are _____

B Choose from the nine words you have made. Write the correct word under each picture.

1 _____ 2 _____ 3 _____ 4 _____

C Complete the sentences, using words you have made.

1 The only sound was the _____ of a mouse.

2 A _____ has four equal sides.

3 _____ the tube of toothpaste gently.

4 I saw a grey _____ eating an acorn in the woods.

5 Please don't sit on mother's hat! You'll _____ it!

D Word meanings

1 American Indian woman	s	q	u			
2 sudden spray of water	s	q	u			
3 short scream	s	q	u			
4 to hold someone tight	s	q	u			
5 small animal with a bushy tail	s	q	u			

tch as in wi**tch**

A Making words

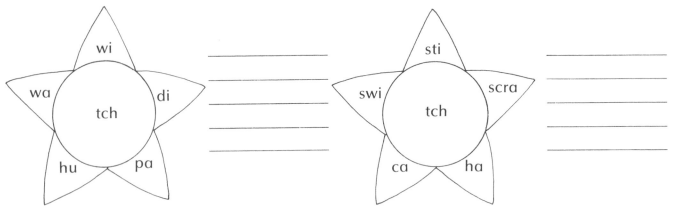

Word sums

bu + tch + er = _____   ki + tch + en = _____

B Choose from the twelve words you have made. Write the correct word under each picture.

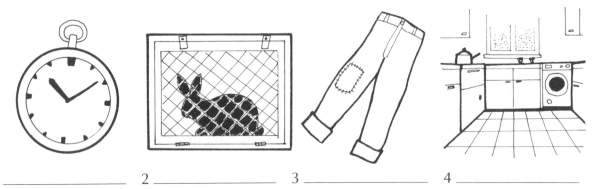

1 _____   2 _____   3 _____   4 _____

C Complete the sentences, using words you have made.

1 The wicked _____ flew away on her broomstick.

2 Please will you _____ on the television?

3 Susan couldn't _____ the ball, so she was out of the game.

4 We hope the robin's eggs will _____ soon.

5 Dad made a new _____ for my pet rabbit.

D Word meanings

1 narrow stream at the side of a road or field

2 slight cut in your skin

3 someone who sells meat

4 to use a needle and thread

5 worn on the wrist to tell the time

6 room where food is prepared

		t	c	h		
				t	c	h
		t	c	h		
			t	c	h	
		t	c	h		
		t	c	h		

Silent b as in comb

A Making words

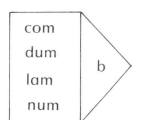

com
dum
lam
num

b

——————————
——————————
——————————
——————————

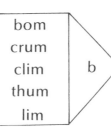

bom
crum
clim
thum
lim

b

——————————
——————————
——————————
——————————
——————————

Word sum

plum + b + er = _____

B Choose from the ten words you have made. Write the correct word under each picture.

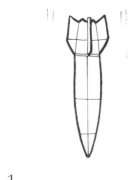

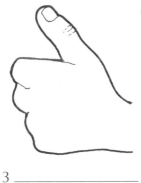

1 _____ 2 _____ 3 _____ 4 _____

C Here is a new code.

b= ■   c= ◇   h= >   i= ▲   l= □

m= △   o= ●   u= ∩   t= ✗

What do these words mean? See if you can decode them.

1 ■ ● △ ■   _____   2 ✗ > ∩ △ ■   _____

3 ◇ □ ▲ △ ■   _____   4 ◇ ● △ ■   _____

D What are they?

1 Someone who mends leaks in pipes is called a _____.

2 A young sheep is called a _____.

3 We say that someone who cannot speak is _____.

4 A _____ is a very small piece of bread or cake.

5 Your fingers go _____ when they are so cold that you cannot feel them.

Silent k as in knee

A Making words

k + nee _____   k + nob _____

    nife _____   neel _____

    night _____   nock _____

    nit _____   not _____

    nuckle _____   now _____

B Choose from the ten words you have made. Write the correct word under each picture.

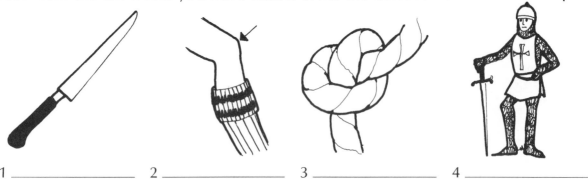

1 _____   2 _____   3 _____   4 _____

C Complete the sentences by choosing the correct word from the brackets.

1 The Queen asked the _____ to _____ on one _____.
(kneel, knight, knee)

2 Can you _____ a half-hitch _____? (knot, knit)

3 Pam does not _____ how to _____. (knit, know)

4 Stephen accidentally cut his _____ on a _____. (knife, knuckle)

5 Please _____ on the door with the brass _____. (knob, knock)

D Word meanings

Across

1 to make something from wool with two needles

2 man who wore armour

3 goes with fork

4 joint of a finger

Down

1 made by tying a piece of string

2 joint in the middle of the leg

3 bang on the door

4 to balance yourself on your knees

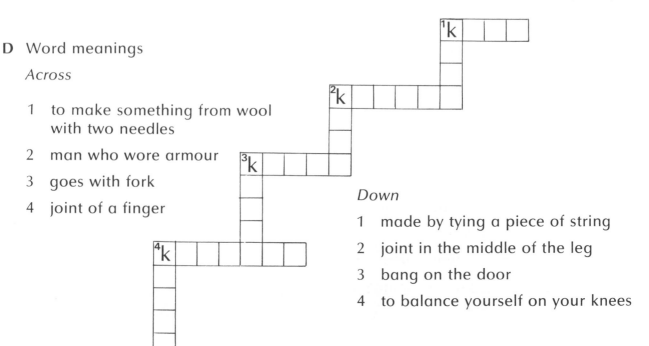

14

Silent l   as in yolk

A   Making words

yo + l + k = _____   fo + l + k   = _____

ca + l + f = _____   ca + l + m   = _____

wa + l + k = _____   pa + l + m   = _____

ha + l + f = _____   cha + l + k   = _____

ta + l + k = _____   sa + l + mon = _____

B   Choose from the ten words you have made. Write the correct word under each picture.

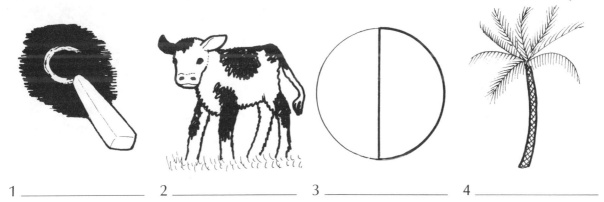

1 _____   2 _____   3 _____   4 _____

C   Complete the sentences, using words you have made.

1   If it's fine on Sunday, we'll go for a _____ in the park.

2   Five pence is exactly _____ of ten pence.

3   Teachers often say, "Don't _____!"

4   The sea was so _____ it looked like a mirror.

5   The fisherman caught a huge _____ yesterday.

D   Word meanings

1   used to write on blackboards

2   old-fashioned word for people

3   young cow or bull

4   yellow part of an egg

5   tree found on tropical islands

6   opposite of rough

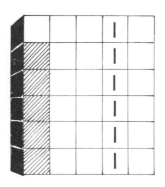

15

Silent w   as in wreck

A Making words

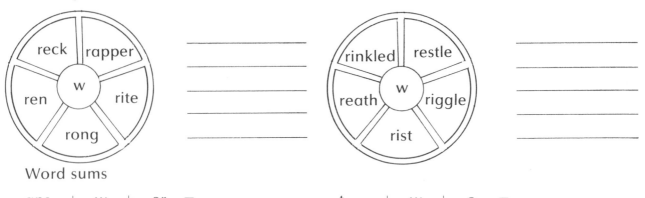

_____
_____
_____
_____
_____

_____
_____
_____
_____
_____

Word sums

ans + w + er = _____   t + w + o = _____

B Choose from the twelve words you have made. Write the correct word under each picture

1 _____   2 _____   3 _____   4 _____

C Complete the sentences, using words you have made.

1 Carlos watched the snake _____ through the grass.

2 Tom fell and broke his _____ .

3 Try to _____ all the questions in half an hour.

4 The old man had a very _____ face.

5 Divers went down to look for the _____ of the ship.

D Word meanings

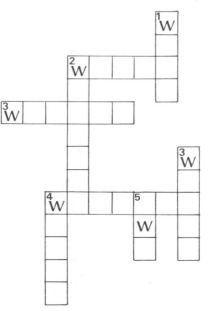

Across

2 put words on paper

3 often hung on a door at Christmas

4 to fight with someone

Down

1 very small bird

2 paper round a sweet

3 ruin of a ship

4 opposite of right

5 one more than one!

16

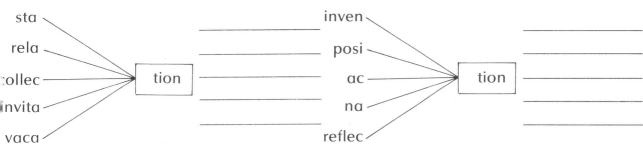

A Making words

sta
rela
collec
invita
vaca
→ **tion** → _____ _____ _____ _____ _____

inven
posi
ac
na
reflec
→ **tion** → _____ _____ _____ _____ _____

frac
conversa
decora
opera
→ **tion** → _____ _____ _____ _____

B Choose from the fourteen words you have made. Write the correct word under each picture.

1 _____   2 _____   3 _____   4 _____

C Complete the sentences, using words you have made.

1 Caroline looked at her _____ in the mirror.

2 Ben held a _____ with Gran on the telephone.

3 Mum drives Dad to the _____ every morning to catch his train.

4 Simon was given a new _____ man for his birthday.

5 The scientist showed off his latest _____.

6 Grandad is going into hospital for an _____.

D Word meanings

1 anyone in your family

2 group of similar articles, e.g. stamps

3 holiday

4 where something is placed

5 people of a country

6 request for you to go somewhere

7 takes place in hospital

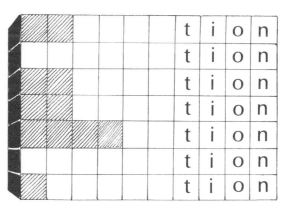

17

dge as in bri**dge**

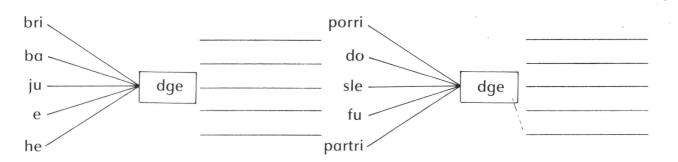

A Making words

bri
ba
ju
e
he

→ dge

_____
_____
_____
_____
_____

porri
do
sle
fu
partri

→ dge

_____
_____
_____
_____
_____

B Choose from the ten words you have made. Write the correct word under each picture.

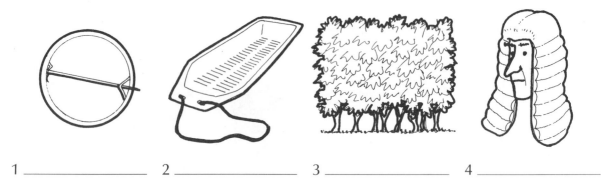

1 _____ 2 _____ 3 _____ 4 _____

C Complete the sentences, using words you have made.

1 It was exciting to drive across the suspension _____.

2 Dad cut the yew _____ into the shape of a bird.

3 The twins slid down the icy slope on their _____.

4 We had _____ for breakfast this morning.

5 Sam stood on the _____ of the pool, then dived in.

D Word meanings

Across

1 'fence' of bushes

4 worn to show membership

5 breakfast cereal made from oats

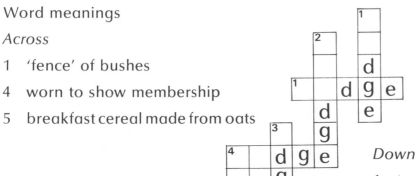
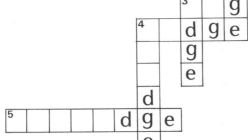

Down

1 to avoid by moving quickly

2 sleigh; toboggan

3 brink; border

4 road crossing a river, railway, etc.

ph as in telephone

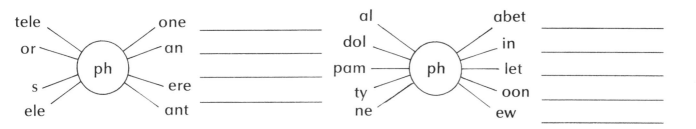

A Making words

tele one _____
or an _____
ph
s ere _____
ele ant _____

al abet _____
dol in _____
pam — ph — let _____
ty oon _____
ne ew _____

Word sums

gra + ph = _____

cenota + ph = _____

photogra + ph = _____

B Choose from the twelve words you have made. Write the correct word under each picture.

1 _____ 2 _____ 3 _____ 4 _____

C Complete the sentences, using words you have made.

1 Barry had his _____ taken at school.

2 Joseph is Philip's uncle, so Philip is Joseph's _____.

3 "Please answer the _____," called mother from the kitchen.

4 There are twenty-six letters in the _____.

5 Class 8 made a bar _____ to show everyone's height.

D Word meanings

1 largest living land animal

2 large, silver-grey sea mammal

3 another word for a ball

4 child whose parents are dead

5 war memorial

6 very, very strong wind

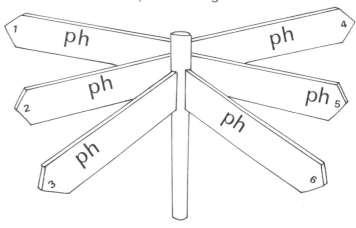

ight as in f**ight**

A Making words

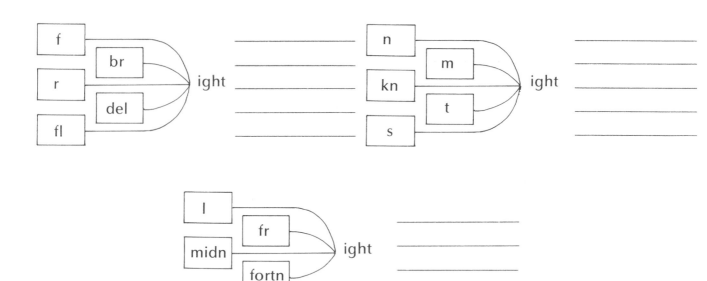

f		
	br	
r		ight
	del	
fl		

_____
_____
_____
_____

n		
	m	
kn		ight
	t	
s		

_____
_____
_____
_____

l		
	fr	
midn		ight
	fortn	

_____
_____
_____

B Choose from the fourteen words you have made. Write the correct word under each picture

1 _____ 2 _____ 3 _____ 4 _____

C Complete the sentences, using words you have made.

1 Jenny is going on holiday to Spain for a _____.

2 Bob couldn't wear his new shoes because they were too _____.

3 Sally _____ have won the race if she hadn't stumbled.

4 A stone is heavy but a feather is _____.

5 The flower gardens are a beautiful _____.

D Word meanings

1 great pleasure; joy; happiness

2 set of stairs

3 sudden shock that scares you

4 opposite of left

5 time between evening and the next morning

			i	g	h	t
			i	g	h	t
			i	g	h	t
		i	g	h	t	
		i	g	h	t	

20

Soft c as in celery

A Making words

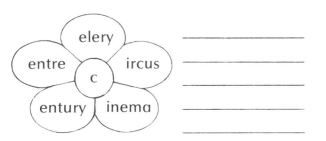

_____
_____
_____
_____

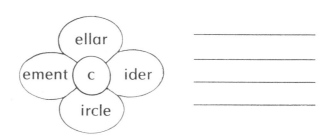

_____
_____
_____
_____

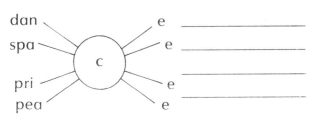

_____
_____
_____
_____

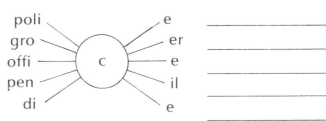

_____
_____
_____
_____
_____

B Choose from the eighteen words you have made. Write the correct word under each picture.

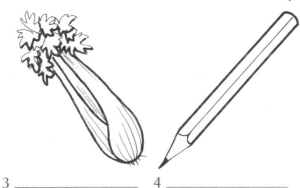

1 _____ 2 _____ 3 _____ 4 _____

C Complete the sentences, using words you have made.

1 The _____ of the book was two pounds.

2 A _____ is a room under the ground.

3 The satellite moved through _____, round and round the earth.

4 You can see clowns, acrobats and animals in a _____.

5 A _____ is a shopkeeper who sells many kinds of food.

D Word meanings

1 ring that is perfectly round

2 one hundred years

3 free from war and fighting of any kind

4 middle point of something

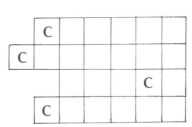

Soft g as in cage

A Making words

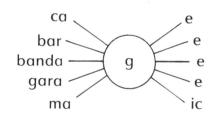
ca ___ e
bar ___ e
banda ___ e
gara ___ e
ma ___ ic

_____
_____
_____
_____
_____
_____

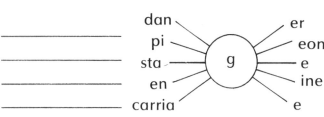
dan ___ er
pi ___ eon
sta ___ e
en ___ ine
carria ___ e

_____
_____
_____
_____
_____
_____

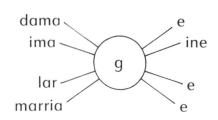
dama ___ e
ima ___ ine
lar ___ e
marria ___ e

_____
_____
_____
_____

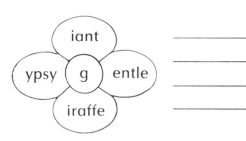
iant
ypsy g entle
iraffe

_____
_____
_____
_____

B Choose from the eighteen words you have made. Write the correct word under each picture

1 _____ 2 _____ 3 _____ 4 _____

C Complete the sentences, using words you have made.

1 Red is the signal for _____.

2 There is a _____ in the story of *Jack and the Beanstalk*.

3 History books help us to _____ life long ago.

4 The heavy rains did much _____ to the farmer's crops.

5 A car has an _____ to make it go.

D Word meanings

1 when a man and a woman become husband and wife

2 place where cars are kept

3 member of a group of people who wander from place to place

4 opposite of little

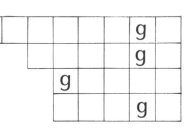

22

Check up　| y　ey |

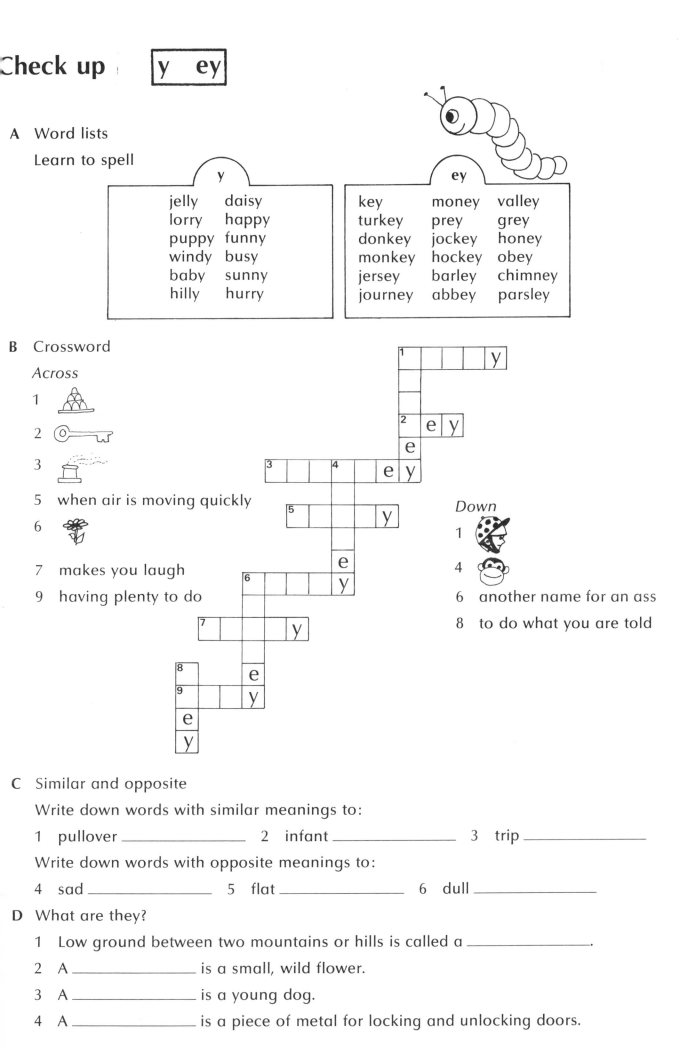

A Word lists

Learn to spell

y

jelly	daisy
lorry	happy
puppy	funny
windy	busy
baby	sunny
hilly	hurry

ey

key	money	valley
turkey	prey	grey
donkey	jockey	honey
monkey	hockey	obey
jersey	barley	chimney
journey	abbey	parsley

B Crossword

Across

1
2
3
5 when air is moving quickly
6
7 makes you laugh
9 having plenty to do

Down

1
4
6 another name for an ass
8 to do what you are told

C Similar and opposite

Write down words with similar meanings to:

1 pullover _____   2 infant _____   3 trip _____

Write down words with opposite meanings to:

4 sad _____   5 flat _____   6 dull _____

D What are they?

1 Low ground between two mountains or hills is called a _____.

2 A _____ is a small, wild flower.

3 A _____ is a young dog.

4 A _____ is a piece of metal for locking and unlocking doors.

23

Check up   ei   ie

A Word lists

Learn to spell

ei

veil	eight	eighty
reign	sleigh	receive
neigh	deceive	veins
reins	reindeer	ceiling
weight	neighbour	seize

ie

chief	achieve	shield
believe	niece	mischief
priest	grief	piece
siege	yield	brief
thief	field	handkerchief

B Crossword

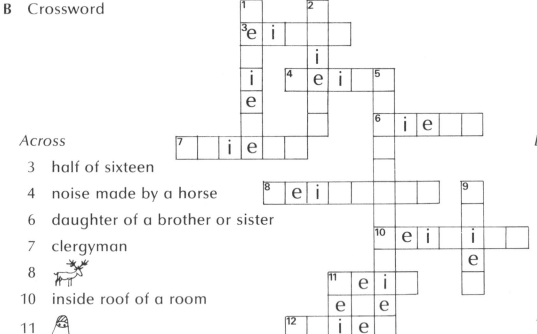

Across

3 half of sixteen

4 noise made by a horse

6 daughter of a brother or sister

7 clergyman

8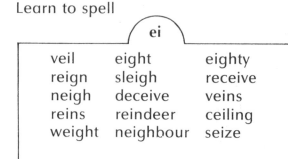

10 inside roof of a room

11

12 short; very quick

Down

1 to think that something is true

2

5 cloth for wiping your nose

9

11 tubes that carry blood towards your heart

C Similar and opposite

Write down words with similar meanings to:

1 accept _____   2 robber _____   3 cheat _____

4 part _____

Write down words with opposite meanings to:

5 happiness _____   6 overcome _____   7 floor _____

8 lengthy _____

D Word meanings

1 A _____ is someone who lives near you.

2 To tell people a lie is to _____ them.

3 To _____ means to give in.

4 If you were in a _____ you would be under attack.

Check up   el | le

A Word lists

Learn to spell

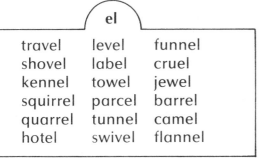

el

travel	level	funnel
shovel	label	cruel
kennel	towel	jewel
squirrel	parcel	barrel
quarrel	tunnel	camel
hotel	swivel	flannel

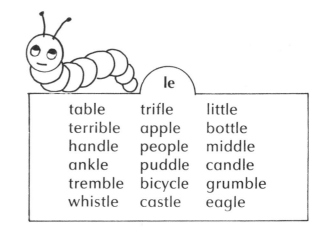

le

table	trifle	little
terrible	apple	bottle
handle	people	middle
ankle	puddle	candle
tremble	bicycle	grumble
whistle	castle	eagle

B Crossword

Across

2

6

9   not big

10   tool like a spade

11   flat and even

12

Down

1

3

4

5   to complain; find fault

6   vehicle with two wheels and pedals

7   building where people pay for a bedroom and food

8   a referee blows one

C Similar and opposite

Write down words with similar meanings to:

1   persons _____   2   shake _____   3   centre _____

Write down words with opposite meanings to:

4   big _____   5   uneven _____   6   kind _____

D What are they?

1   A _____ is a desert animal which can go for a long time without water.

2   An _____ is a large bird of prey.

3   A _____ can be found on a ship or on a steam engine.

4   _____ is a pudding made from jelly, fruit, custard and cream.

Check up   Silent b k l w

A Word lists

Learn to spell

b		k		l		w	
comb	bomb	knee	knob	yolk	folk	wreck	wrapper
dumb	crumb	knife	kneel	calf	calm	wrong	wrist
lamb	climb	knight	knock	walk	palm	wreath	wriggle
numb	thumb	knit	knot	half	chalk	write	wrestle
plumber	limb	knuckle	know	talk	salmon	wren	wrinkled
						two	answer

B Hidden in the squares below are seventeen words which contain the silent letters 'k', 'b', 'l' c 'w'. Search across and down for them and ring them.
Write down the words as you find them. The first one has been done for you.

b	r	k	n	i	f	e	i	c	a	y	a
n	w	n	k	i	o	s	a	l	m	o	n
w	r	i	n	k	l	e	d	i	p	l	s
r	o	g	o	t	k	h	u	m	a	k	w
i	n	h	c	t	h	u	m	b	l	i	e
s	g	t	k	b	o	m	b	n	m	k	r
t	w	o	l	k	n	u	c	k	l	e	l

1 _____knife_____   2 _____
3 _____   4 _____
5 _____   6 _____
7 _____   8 _____
9 _____   10 _____
11 _____   12 _____
13 _____   14 _____
15 _____   16 _____
17 _____

C Similar meanings

Write down words with similar meanings to:

1 spoil _____   2 double _____   3 smooth _____

4 squirm _____   5 morsel _____

6 speechless _____   7 people _____   8 bang _____

9 handle _____

D What are they?

1 A young elephant is called a _____.

2 A young sheep is called a _____.

3 A _____ is a large fish.

4 A _____ is a tiny bird.

5 Inside every egg there is a _____.

Check up | tion   dge |

A Word lists

Learn to spell

tion

station	invention
relation	position
collection	action
invitation	nation
vacation	reflection
fraction	decoration
conversation	operation

dge

bridge	hedge
badge	porridge
judge	dodge
edge	sledge
fudge	partridge

B Hidden in the squares below are fourteen words which contain the letters 'dge' and 'tion'. Search across and down for them and ring them.
Write down the words as you find them. The first one has been done for you.

i	s	l	e	d	g	e	t	v	h	i	p	n	k
h	c	o	n	v	e	r	s	a	t	i	o	n	i
e	l	b	a	d	g	e	t	c	o	v	r	e	b
d	a	c	t	i	o	n	a	a	r	y	r	a	n
g	b	r	i	d	g	e	t	t	b	u	i	t	l
e	a	d	o	d	g	e	i	i	j	u	d	g	e
m	n	o	n	t	s	u	o	o	e	d	g	e	r
r	e	l	a	t	i	o	n	n	e	y	e	e	t

1 ___sledge___   2 _____
3 _____   4 _____
5 _____   6 _____
7 _____   8 _____
9 _____   10 _____
11 _____   12 _____
13 _____   14 _____

C Codes

If a = 1, b = 2, c = 3, and so on, decode the following sentences:

1   4, 18, 1, 23   1   10, 21, 4, 7, 5   15, 14   1   2, 18, 9, 4, 7, 5

_____ ___ _____ _____ ___ _____

5, 1, 20, 9, 14, 7   16, 15, 18, 18, 9, 4, 7, 5.

_____   _____.

2   4, 18, 1, 23   1   18, 5, 12, 1, 20, 9, 15, 14   1, 20   20, 8, 5

_____ ___ _____ _____ _____

19, 20, 1, 20, 9, 15, 14.

_____.

D Can you sort out these muddled words?

1 gdbae _____   2 gldees _____   3 degeh _____

4 feelcrnoit _____   5 lltnocieoc _____

6 nnntiievo _____

27

Check up | ph   ight |

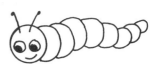

A Word lists

Learn to spell

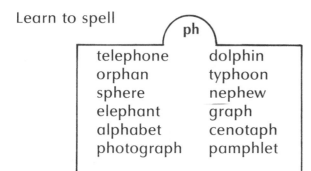

ph

telephone	dolphin
orphan	typhoon
sphere	nephew
elephant	graph
alphabet	cenotaph
photograph	pamphlet

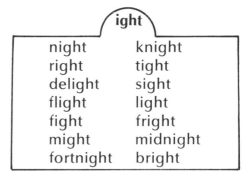

ight

night	knight
right	tight
delight	sight
flight	light
fight	fright
might	midnight
fortnight	bright

B Criss-cross word

Begin with the clue for 1 *Down*.

Down

1 picture taken with a camera

Across

1

2 close-fitting

3 like a hurricane

4 two weeks

5

6 12 o'clock at night

7

8 begins with a, ends with z

9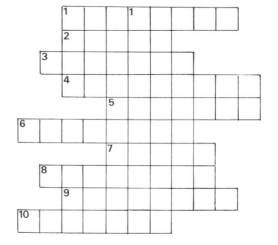

10 joy; happiness

C Similar and opposite

Write down words with similar meanings to:

1 ball _____   2 war memorial _____   3 shock _____

Write down words with opposite meanings to:

4 day _____   5 left _____   6 dark _____

D Can you sort out these muddled words?

1 trgih _____   2 hfglit _____   3 hgist _____

4 inghkt _____   5 eeehlpotn _____   6 whepen _____